Carlota's Cooking Class

Arianne Weber

Illustrated by Diane Palmisciano

Rigby®

Carlota came home from cooking class
feeling sad.
She had been excited about taking the
class because her best friend Marisol
was taking it, too.

"Is something wrong, Carlota?"
her mother asked.

Carlota told her mother about the food
they were cooking in class.

"There's nothing fun to eat!"
Carlota exclaimed.
"I asked Ms. Lopez if we could make
pizza, but she said that we couldn't
make everyone's favorite food."

Carlota's mother smiled.
"Maybe you'll cook something
you like next week.
Let's just wait."

Carlota arrived at the next cooking class,
hoping that they would make something good.

"Hello, everyone.
It's hot tonight, so I thought
that we would make a cold treat,"
Ms. Lopez said.

Ms. Lopez started
to pass out the recipes.
The students were sure it would be
something boring, like cold soup.

"It's ice cream!" Ben called out
as he read the recipe.

"It's true," Carlota told Marisol
after she looked at it.
They both loved ice cream.

Ms. Lopez taped a copy of the recipe
to the wall near the refrigerator.
Then she put all the ingredients
on the table so that everyone
could see them.

Ice Cream

1 cup milk

2 tablespoons sugar

$\frac{1}{2}$ teaspoon vanilla

1 pint plastic bag with zipper lock

1 gallon plastic bag with zipper lock

6 tablespoons rock salt

ice

- Pour milk, sugar, and vanilla into the small bag and close the bag tightly.
- Fill half of the large bag with ice and add salt.
- Put the small bag inside the large bag and close the large bag.
- Turn the bag over again and again, until the milk turns into ice.

Ms. Lopez divided the class
into pairs, so Carlota and Marisol
worked together.
Each pair was in charge of one part
of the recipe.

"Carlota, you and Marisol
need to make sure
that we have enough milk
for everyone's ice cream.
We need 1 cup of milk
for each person,"
Ms. Lopez said.

"There are 16 people here,"
Carlota said, "so we'll need
16 cups of milk."

They walked over to the table
where Ms. Lopez had put the milk.
"That looks like a lot more than
16 cups of milk," said Marisol.

"This says that it is 1 quart," Carlota said,
picking up one of the milk cartons.
"How can we figure out how many quarts
we'll need to get 16 cups?"

Carlota and Marisol were quiet
as they considered the problem.
Since the whole recipe depended on
how much milk they used,
they didn't want to make a mistake!

"First we have to find out how many cups there are in a quart," Carlota said.

She filled a measuring cup with water and poured it into a quart jug. Marisol and Carlota counted 4 cups to fill the jug.

"There are 4 cups in a quart," explained Marisol. "Since 4 times 4 equals 16, and we need 16 cups, we'll need 4 quarts of milk."

Carlota and Marisol took turns
measuring milk
for everyone's ice cream.

"Thank you for telling us
that there are 4 cups in a quart,"
said Ms. Lopez.

14

Carlota and Marisol had fun
mixing the ingredients together,
flipping them over again and again
in the large bag.

"I can feel the milk turning
into ice cream," said Carlota
as she rolled the bag.
She couldn't wait to taste
what they had made.

When Carlota's mother picked her up
after class, Carlota was smiling.

"It seems like you had a good time
at cooking class tonight,"
her mother said.
"What did you make?"

"We made ice cream," said Carlota.
"Now I'll never complain
about cooking class again!"